Little Rhymers

Edited By Jenni Harrison

First published in Great Britain in 2020 by:

Young Writers
Remus House
Coltsfoot Drive
Peterborough
PE2 9BF
Telephone: 01733 890066
Website: www.youngwriters.co.uk

Printed and bound in the UK by BookPrintingUK
Website: www.bookprintinguk.com
YB0429A

Dear Reader,

Welcome to a fun-filled book of acrostic poems!

Here at Young Writers, we are delighted to introduce our new poetry competition for KS1 pupils, *My First Acrostic: All About Me.* Acrostic poems are an enjoyable way to introduce pupils to the world of poetry and allow the young writer to open their imagination to a range of topics of their choice. The colourful and engaging entry forms allowed even the youngest (or most reluctant) of pupils to create a poem using the acrostic technique, and with that, encouraged them to include other literary techniques such as similes and description. Here at Young Writers we are passionate about introducing the love and art of creative writing to the next generation and we love being a part of their journey.

From pets to family, from hobbies to idols, these pupils have shaped and crafted their ideas brilliantly, showcasing their budding creativity. So, we invite you to proceed through these pages and take a glimpse into these blossoming young writers' minds. We hope you will relish these poems as much as we have.

contents

Lyla Nora Dickinson (5)   68
Jada Sherriff (6)   69

Golborne Community Primary School, Golborne

Beau-Lily Kathleen Dennis (6)   70
Jessica Anne Taylor (6)   71
Isabelle Hannah Critchley (6)   72
Elias James Griffiths (7)   73
Anthony Gregor James Crane (6)   74
Felix Joaquin Murray (6)   75
Lucas Joel Jackson (7)   76
Sophie Dumville (6)   77
Darcey Reay (6)   78
Harvey Poole (6)   79
Megan Elizabeth Watkins (6)   80
Shannon Hill (6)   81
Cody Cooper (6)   82
Emelia Fairclough (6)   83
Leo Terence Ashton (7)   84
April Jones (7)   85
Tia Jessica Markland (6)   86
Skye Dean (6)   87

Perry Wood Primary & Nursery School, Worcester

Annalise Wilkes (6)   88
Mia Olszak (6)   89
Keeley Louise Thomas (6)   90
Kamila Ivenkova (7) & Lena   91
Amelia Dubiel-Jasinska
Jessica Dobbins (7)   92
Melisa (6)   93
Owura Yaw Quashie (6)   94
Alexander Longshaw (6)   95
Olivia Ann Davis (6)   96
Lacie Broughton (6)   97
Maddison Grant (6)   98
Kasey Jay Morris (6)   99
Joshua Mason (6)   100
Ivy Smith (6)   101

Ramsgate Holy Trinity CE (A) Primary School, Broadstairs

Max Maclean (7)   102
George William Cox (6)   103
Olivia Grace Garratt (7)   104
Poppy Maclean (7)   105
Alice Guan (6)   106
Lola Mathews (6)   107
Georgia Louise Youngs (7)   108
Esmée Rose Denton (6)   109
Amber Thompson (6)   110
Emily Batcheler (6)   111
Zach Ryan Evans-Hunt (6)   112
Finlay Collins (6)   113
Peter Tovell (6)   114
Freya June Maxted (6)   115
Samuel Kane (6)   116
Evelyn Michael (7)   117
Liam Cannon (6)   118
Dolcie Thorn (6)   119
Finlay McAlister (6)   120
James Bryan Greensted (6)   121
Teddy Meise (7)   122

St James' Primary School, Paisley

Ayomide Roland (6)   123
Aaron McEwan (6)   124
Cameron Thomson (6)   125
Robyn Borris (5)   126
Zack Nugent (6)   127
Liam Sweeney (6)   128
Ross McFadyen (5)   129
Keira Reader (6)   130
David Adetoyosi Adekanmbi (6)   131
Logan Flanagan (6)   132
Lara Reis (6)   133
Tye David McLeod (6)   134
Ben Deatcher (6)   135

Yealmpstone Farm Primary School, Plympton

Millie Jones (6)	136
Oliver Sluman (6)	137
Leighton Sindall (7)	138
Lilah-Rose Hobbs (6)	139
Harrison Smith (6)	140
Seth Jonathan Williams (6)	141
Olivia Gibson (6)	142
Evie Stemp (7)	143
Matthew Jones (7)	144
Eve Leia Hanrahan (6)	145
Sophie Nightingale (6)	146
Scarlett Evans (7)	147
Taylor Holmes (6)	148
Evie Lilgan (6)	149
Emilia Mills (6)	150
Freya Deady (6)	151
Faith Ella English (7)	152
Eloise Walker (6)	153
Ben Robinson (7)	154
Finley Mark Whiting (7)	155

The Poems

Connor Delaney

C onnor is amazing
O h, Connor's family is amazing
N o girls allowed in my house
N ot my best friend
O h my gosh
R ead on the carpet

D oing work
E is in the alphabet
L oon on the Moon is a book
A huge elephant in the zoo
N o Xbox for a week for me
E vie is my best friend
Y ou are my best friend.

Connor Delaney (6)

Five Lanes Primary School, Upper Wortley

Fern Craven

F antastic at gymnastics
E verything is amazing
R emember everybody's birthday
N ice people are my friends, I like them

C hocolate is my favourite snack
R ed is a pretty colour
A unicorn is my favourite animal
V ery good at listening to Mrs Pearce
E veryone plays in the sun
N ice people are my friends.

Fern Eva Craven (6)
Five Lanes Primary School, Upper Wortley

Faith Taylor

F abulous and helpful and also kind and happy
A unicorn is my favourite animal
I t is a nice day
T alking to my friends every day
H ow do you feel?

T ea is nice
A rt is my favourite thing to do
Y ou are beautiful
L isten to the teacher
O liver is my best friend
R emember the 5th of November.

Faith Taylor (6)
Five Lanes Primary School, Upper Wortley

Daisy

D og is called Luna
A unicorn is my favourite animal
I love to do gymnastics
S o good at maths
Y ellow is my favourite colour

E very day I play with my friends
V ery good at listening to Miss Pearce
A seagull steals my chips at the seaside
N ice friend to everybody
S o kind and caring.

Daisy Beau Evans (7)

Five Lanes Primary School, Upper Wortley

Zachary Judge

Z ach is like The Flash
A cts like a monkey all the time
C ars are fast
H orns are tough
A mazing child
R ests like a monster
Y eets everything

J elly is the best
U nderstands everything
D addies drink beer
G oes on bike rides
E verything is amazing.

Zachary Judge (7)
Five Lanes Primary School, Upper Wortley

Belle Grace

B eautiful girl
E xcellent clever person
L ovely, always helpful little girl
L ittle, kind, funny little girl
E xcellent, clever girl

G ood at Miss Pearce's lovely maths
R eading every day at home
A mazing author
C lever person at ICT
E ncouraging people to be nice.

Belle Howitt (6)
Five Lanes Primary School, Upper Wortley

Josh Hyde

J elly is really tasty because it's red and juicy

O ctopuses are underwater

S wimming is a fantastic place

H ot day at the seaside

H ot and sunny day

Y ellow pretty fence

D ark and stormy night

E very day I play with my friends.

Joshua Hyde-Sykes (6)

Five Lanes Primary School, Upper Wortley

Evie-Rose Reed Carrack

E veryone is nice to me
V alentine's Day is so good
I ce cream makes me have brain freeze
E nglish is amazing

R oses are so beautiful
O ranges are disgusting
S it down when you come in from playtime
E verybody is kind to me.

Evie-Rose Reed Carrack (6)

Five Lanes Primary School, Upper Wortley

Scarlett

S carlet is a shade of red
C anada is my favourite country
A mazing manners in school
R iding a gorgeous, fast horse
L illies are a type of flower
E xercise is my hobby
T ickling my sister makes her laugh
T alking to my family.

Scarlett Cosgrove (6)
Five Lanes Primary School, Upper Wortley

Elliot Lee

E lephants are big

L asers are on

L aser-tag is a game

I love animals

O nions taste horrible

T ongues are reddish-pink

L ike to play video games

E lephants are funny

E lephants are brave.

Elliot Williams (7)

Five Lanes Primary School, Upper Wortley

Dylan Hunter

D elighted
Y ou are polite
L ike the school
A mazing
N ice

H ome is good
U p on a ride
N ice to Ollie
T o rugby training
E ven faster than Zack
R ugby.

Dylan Hunter Thompson (5)

Five Lanes Primary School, Upper Wortley

Everything

H orses are soft
A mazing unicorn
L ove Ella
L augh Ella
E gg chicken

D inosaur egg
O strich dinosaur
L ove Mummy
A mazing Ella
N anny is amazing.

Halle Anne Grace Dolan (5)

Five Lanes Primary School, Upper Wortley

Ava

A unicorn is my favourite animal
V ery good at listening
A seagull steals my chips

M agnificent at being helpful
A mazing at maths
E very day I play with my friends.

Ava Weldon (6)

Five Lanes Primary School, Upper Wortley

Me

S anta lives in the North Pole

I love cake and milkshakes

E nglish is my favourite

N ice people give things

N ice people live in school

A ntarctica is very cold.

Sienna Lakin (6)

Five Lanes Primary School, Upper Wortley

Abigail

A bigail is an angel in the sky
B eing grumpy
I love school
G orgeous Abigail
A bigail is amazing and very smart
I love everyone
L ove Miss Low.

Abigail Tait (6)

Five Lanes Primary School, Upper Wortley

Abigail

A bigail is amazing

B illy is amazing

I am amazing

G ot a big quilt

A big quilt is smart

I am amazing in maths

L ibby is star for the day.

Abigail Jane Jarvis (6)

Five Lanes Primary School, Upper Wortley

Dexter

D exter's dog likes to jump

E very dog is crazy

X mas is my favourite part

T otally awesome dog

E veryone likes Cash

R unning is my favourite.

Dexter Alfred Vasey (6)

Five Lanes Primary School, Upper Wortley

Animals

J olly koalas
O ctopuses have wiggly tentacles
C ats have fur
E lephants are grey
L ittle animals, mouse
Y ellow birds
N ice animals.

Jocelyn Tse-Leach (5)
Five Lanes Primary School, Upper Wortley

Oliver

O n some days I go to the park
L ucas Montgomery is nice
I t was a nice day
V ery good Oliver
E very day I do my spelling
R eading silently.

Oliver John Charles Millington (6)

Five Lanes Primary School, Upper Wortley

Animals

A nimals are cool
R hinos are tough
T igers eat meat
H ippos are fat
U nder the sea is a pufferfish
R attlesnakes live in grass.

Arthur Paul Walker (5)

Five Lanes Primary School, Upper Wortley

Millie

M um played with me
I walked to the park
L ots of us went back for dinner
L ovely ice cream too
I love my mummy
E very day!

Millie May Blakey (5)

Five Lanes Primary School, Upper Wortley

Jaxson

J axson is awesome
A lways happy
X mas is my favourite time
S peedy on my bike
O n Wednesday I go to Beavers
N ever gives up.

Jaxson Hargreaves (7)
Five Lanes Primary School, Upper Wortley

Billy

B illy is smart and daring
I am brilliant at hiding
L ittle brothers give high fives
L ibby is a girl
Y ellow is a bright colour.

Billy Barlow (7)

Five Lanes Primary School, Upper Wortley

Bilal Sharif

B ilal is good at maths
I n English, I write fun poems
L ike to play teachers
A live on the top of the hill
L ike to play football

Bilal Mohammad Sharif (6)

Five Lanes Primary School, Upper Wortley

Millie

M y cat is soft

I like kittens

L ike to go outside

L oving my mum

I s great

E very day I cuddle my kitten.

Millie Rose Robinson (5)

Five Lanes Primary School, Upper Wortley

Riley

R eads lots of books

I s very good at boxing

L oves to play

E ats lots of ice cream

Y ou are lucky to be his friend.

Riley Bagshaw (6)

Five Lanes Primary School, Upper Wortley

Connor

C onnor is here today

O nly likes football

N ice to friends

N ever gives up

O ne cool dude

R eally good.

Connor Gledhill (6)

Five Lanes Primary School, Upper Wortley

Tallulah

T alented
A mazing
L ovely
L ovely
U nderstanding
L aughs a lot
A wesome
H appy.

Tallulah-Audrina Duffy Shaw (6)

Five Lanes Primary School, Upper Wortley

28

Seth

S wimming is my favourite hobby
E ating pizza is yummy
T ickling my brother makes him laugh
H opping is my favourite sport.

Seth Porter (7)

Five Lanes Primary School, Upper Wortley

Libbie

L ovely cake
I love pandas
B aby pups are cute
B ad Chloe is my sister
I am kind
E ven I am silly.

Libbie Reid (7)

Five Lanes Primary School, Upper Wortley

Daniel

D ad is funny
A merica is a country
N ever be bad
I like blue
E vie isn't here
L ove Miss Lowe.

Daniel Procter (6)

Five Lanes Primary School, Upper Wortley

Lucas

L ovely handwriting
U nbelievable gaming
C ars are fast like me
A n apple tree is in my garden
S uper at rugby.

Lucas Hancock (6)

Five Lanes Primary School, Upper Wortley

Jaxson

J axson caught Pikachu

A nd Charmander

X -ray Charizard

S cary fire

O h no

N ot the big Charizard.

Jaxson Kisby (5)

Five Lanes Primary School, Upper Wortley

Me

L ovely manners around
U nder my bed is a dancing spider
C at is kind
A ntarctica
S nakes slither around.

Lucas (7)

Five Lanes Primary School, Upper Wortley

Ebony

E bony likes baby dolls

B rilliant at numbers

O utside she plays around

N oisy and

Y ou will like her.

Ebony-Alice Tillett (6)

Five Lanes Primary School, Upper Wortley

Mikey

M y dog is a Westie
I like to play with my dog
K eys are shiny
E ggs are healthy
Y ou look like me.

Mikey Jaden Fusco (6)

Five Lanes Primary School, Upper Wortley

Noah H

N oah is amazing
O nly likes hot dogs
A m a good boy
H orses are the best

H elpful and kind.

Noah Hudson (6)
Five Lanes Primary School, Upper Wortley

Maya

M y mummy is helping me
A ntonina is my best friend
Y ou're my best teacher
A pples are my favourite food.

Maya Cygan (5)

Five Lanes Primary School, Upper Wortley

Lexi

L ovely kind girl

E lephants are my favourite animal

X mas is my favourite holiday

I love my family a lot.

Lexi-May Bolton (7)
Five Lanes Primary School, Upper Wortley

Cody

C lever, smart and kind

O bviously I am gorgeous

D o lots of hard work

Y oghurt is my favourite snack.

Cody Bradley Hopps (6)

Five Lanes Primary School, Upper Wortley

Noah

N ever shout out

O ver the night I saw a dog

A rt is the best subject ever

H orror movies are haunted.

Noah Harrington (6)

Five Lanes Primary School, Upper Wortley

My Thoughts

O striches are cool
L ike Mrs Jobson
L ike Leighton
I nteresting Halle
E lephants are fat.

Ollie Butler (5)

Five Lanes Primary School, Upper Wortley

Tilly

T illy is intelligent
I ntelligent and always
L aughing
L ovely and
Y ou will like her!

Tilly Wheelhouse (5)

Five Lanes Primary School, Upper Wortley

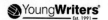

Kane

K ind and thoughtful
A lways practises his spellings
N ever gives up
E very day he plays football.

Kane Maxamillian Warren (7)
Five Lanes Primary School, Upper Wortley

Rafael

R espectful

A mazing

F antastic

A ce

E verybody is my friend

L ove my mum.

Rafael Ikekhua (5)

Five Lanes Primary School, Upper Wortley

Jake

J ake is good at football
A frica is good I think
K ind Jake is happy
E lephants squirt water.

Jake Firth (6)

Five Lanes Primary School, Upper Wortley

Reuban

R euban is
E xciting
U nderstanding
B ooster pack
A mazing and
N eat.

Reuban Singh Chana (5)

Five Lanes Primary School, Upper Wortley

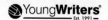

Billy

B lue sea at the seaside
I n Filey
L ots of seagulls
L icking ice cream
Y um!

Billy Brow (6)

Five Lanes Primary School, Upper Wortley

Hope

H obby is swimming

O ne baby sister

P igs are my favourite animal

E lephants are great.

Hope Mary Wood (7)

Five Lanes Primary School, Upper Wortley

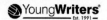

Hadiya

H appy
A good friend
D elightful
I ntelligent
Y oung
A wesome.

Hadiya Fatima Sharif (5)
Five Lanes Primary School, Upper Wortley

Things I Like

R unning races

O llie is fast

M inion

A pple

H ouse

N inja.

Romahn Asim Ali (5)

Five Lanes Primary School, Upper Wortley

Lucas

L et's talk about fish
U nderwater
C olourful
A mazing
S wimmers.

Lucas Garrett (6)
Five Lanes Primary School, Upper Wortley

Murray

    M urray
    U nderstanding
W **R** iting
    R unning
    A ce
    Y oung.

Murray Stephen Dunbar (5)
Five Lanes Primary School, Upper Wortley

Kian

K ind to my friends
I love football
A pples are healthy
N ever gives up.

Kian Patterson (6)

Five Lanes Primary School, Upper Wortley

Vicky

V ery kind
I like to play with my sister
C alm
K ind
Y oung.

Vicky L (6)
Five Lanes Primary School, Upper Wortley

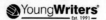

Ella

E lla is

L ovely and always good

L oves her daddy

A nd her breakfast.

Ella Hartley (5)

Five Lanes Primary School, Upper Wortley

Holly

H appy
O nly child
L ove and care
L oving
Y ou look nice.

Holly Trenholm (6)

Five Lanes Primary School, Upper Wortley

Riley

R elaxed

I like Chinese

L oving

E njoy ice cream

Y oung.

Riley Austin Illingworth (5)

Five Lanes Primary School, Upper Wortley

Faith

F abulous
A mazing
I nteresting
T alented dancer
H appy.

Faith Telford Crooks (6)
Five Lanes Primary School, Upper Wortley

Keira

K ind
E nergetic
I rish dancer
R eally clever
A mazing.

Keira Sherriff (6)

Five Lanes Primary School, Upper Wortley

Skye

S ing songs
K ind and bad
Y ellow is my favourite
E at the dinner.

Skye Jade Beaumont (6)

Five Lanes Primary School, Upper Wortley

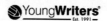

Zack

Z ack is amazing
A nd I am good at games
C lumsy and
K ind.

Zack Hudson (6)

Five Lanes Primary School, Upper Wortley

Harry

H appy
A friend
R unning
R elaxing
Y ummy.

Harry E (5)

Five Lanes Primary School, Upper Wortley

Nate

N ice
A loving friend
T ennis player
E njoy the iPad.

Nate P (5)

Five Lanes Primary School, Upper Wortley

Isla

I like chocolate
S weeties
L ove my mummy
A mazing.

Isla M (5)

Five Lanes Primary School, Upper Wortley

Seb

S cary Charizard

E xplode Pikachu

B elieve in Pokémon.

Sebastian George McMaster (5)

Five Lanes Primary School, Upper Wortley

Theodore

T he scary Pikachu

H orse

E gg

O n the trail.

Theodore Mulligan (5)

Five Lanes Primary School, Upper Wortley

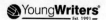

Lyla

L yla is
Y our friend
L ovely
A nd friendly.

Lyla Nora Dickinson (5)
Five Lanes Primary School, Upper Wortley

Jada

J olly Jada
A mazing
D ancer
A wesome.

Jada Sherriff (6)
Five Lanes Primary School, Upper Wortley

Truth

B aby brothers are cute
E very day I play with my friends
A lways eat yummy chocolate
U mbrellas are good for me when it is raining

L ying in bed is my favourite thing
I love my mummy
L oving is my favourite thing to do
Y ellow bright, sunny days are my favourite.

Beau-Lily Kathleen Dennis (6)
Golborne Community Primary School, Golborne

Jessica

J am is the best

E ggs are the worst because they are squishy and sloppy

S ofia is my best amazing friend

S pice is the worst because it is too spicy

I hate squishy yellow bananas

C ake is the best

A giant pink unicorn is my favourite animal because they are pretty.

Jessica Anne Taylor (6)
Golborne Community Primary School, Golborne

Isabelle

I love school, it is good
S eeing the sun makes me happy
A t playtime, I play with my good friends
B eing with my dudes makes me happy
E lephants are my favourite animals
L ove my big dogs
L ove my small cats
E veryone is nice.

Isabelle Hannah Critchley (6)

Golborne Community Primary School, Golborne

Elias

E ggs I don't like because they are slimy and sticky

L ions are the best animal

I don't like stepping in mud

A lways playing Minecraft with my sister

S wimming is the best because I am in Stage Four.

Elias James Griffiths (7)

Golborne Community Primary School, Golborne

Anthony

A nts are my favourite
N eed dinner, so I don't get hungry
T rains are my best toy
H appy gnomes are in my garden
O n Saturday I got a toy
N ever eating sweets
Y ummy food is good.

Anthony Gregor James Crane (6)

Golborne Community Primary School, Golborne

Felix

F ootball is my favourite

E lias is my best friend

L ollipops are my best food

I sabelle is helpful and kind

e **X** tra spicy curry is my favourite

M osquitoes are funny at the zoo.

Felix Joaquin Murray (6)

Golborne Community Primary School, Golborne

Lucas

L ove my new rugby kit

U mbrellas I use when it's raining

C hocolate I love as a snack, so yummy and nice

A brother I play with all day long

S un is what I love on a day at the beach.

Lucas Joel Jackson (7)

Golborne Community Primary School, Golborne

Sophie

S unny hot days are my favourite

O n cold days it is the best day

P ears are my favourite snack

H orses are interesting

I love people who are nice

E lephants are cute.

Sophie Dumville (6)

Golborne Community Primary School, Golborne

Darcey

D ancing is my favourite
A pples are really good
R unning is my favourite
C olouring is my favourite
E ating sweets all day long
Y ummy chocolate is my favourite.

Darcey Reay (6)
Golborne Community Primary School, Golborne

Harvey

H arry Potter is my favourite book
A pples are the best
R ed is my favourite colour
V ans are amazing
E lephants are my favourite
Y ellow makes me happy.

Harvey Poole (6)
Golborne Community Primary School, Golborne

Megan

M ummy is my favourite
E gg is my favourite food
G oing to Starbucks is fun
A chocolate cake is my favourite pudding
N anna is my best nan, because she is pretty.

Megan Elizabeth Watkins (6)

Golborne Community Primary School, Golborne

Shannon

S weets make me smile

H ome is full of love

A pples I like

N an is nice

N aughty Jamie, my brother

O ranges too

N ever eat smelly cheese.

Shannon Hill (6)

Golborne Community Primary School, Golborne

Cody

C ourtney is the best big sister ever
O ctober I am making a rainbow chocolate cake
D iving in a big blue sea makes me smile
Y ellow is my favourite colour.

Cody Cooper (6)

Golborne Community Primary School, Golborne

Emelia

E veryone in my family is so nice
M y mum is beautiful
E lla I love
L ola is my best dog
I love Isabelle
A pples are my favourite.

Emelia Fairclough (6)
Golborne Community Primary School, Golborne

Leo

L ions are my favourite animal
E verybody is my friend
O ceans are the best because they are at the beach

A piece of chocolate makes me smile.

Leo Terence Ashton (7)
Golborne Community Primary School, Golborne

April

A lways watching TV
P hone is the best
R ude people make me sad
I n the zoo, I see a stripy black tiger
L ove meeting new, kind people.

April Jones (7)

Golborne Community Primary School, Golborne

Tia

T ig is my favourite game ever
I love my long pet snake called Coco
A t home, I sleep a lot

M cDonald's is my favourite place.

Tia Jessica Markland (6)
Golborne Community Primary School, Golborne

Skye

S wimming is my favourite sport
K elsey is my best friend
Y o-yos are my favourite toy
E melia is the bestest friend in the world.

Skye Dean (6)

Golborne Community Primary School, Golborne

Unicorn Girl

U niform for school
N est with little chirping birds
I t was a gloomy night
C up of tea is my drink
O tters are my favourite
R oaring animals are scary
N uts are hard to eat

G irls are nice to me
I am loving times tables
R ude children are not nice
L ittle cats are cute.

Annalise Wilkes (6)
Perry Wood Primary & Nursery School, Worcester

Unicorn

U nder the sky is fun

N aughty girl

I ce creams are yummy

C hocolate is very delicious

O ctober is the best month

R eady, steady, go

N ice hot day.

Mia Olszak (6)

Perry Wood Primary & Nursery School, Worcester

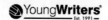

Unicorn

U se your tongue to lick it
N ice ice cream, yum
I ce is very cold
C ows make milk
O ctober is the best month
R ude children
N ight-time is scary.

Keeley Louise Thomas (6)

Perry Wood Primary & Nursery School, Worcester

Friends

F unny jokers

R ide the bike

I t is fun

E asy to ride a bike

N ever stop playing

D rawing on a piece of paper

S aturday and Sunday we play.

Kamila Ivenkova (7) & Lena Amelia Dubiel-Jasinska

Perry Wood Primary & Nursery School, Worcester

Jessica

J ess is sunny
E veryone is kind to me
S o I read a story
S o I went to bed
I am so noisy
C ould be quieter
A utumn is the best.

Jessica Dobbins (7)

Perry Wood Primary & Nursery School, Worcester

Melisa

M um is a lovely parent
E ating a delicious cake
L et my mum sit
I s my mum there?
S un is a perfect thing
A nd we should all love our mums.

Melisa (6)

Perry Wood Primary & Nursery School, Worcester

London

L ondon Eye is amazing

O ranges are yummy

N o war in London, don't be afraid

D on't be afraid

O n a big red bus

N obody here.

Owura Yaw Quashie (6)

Perry Wood Primary & Nursery School, Worcester

Kamila

K ick the ball
A corns are on the trees
M ake a cake
I ce is slippery
L adybirds are small
A eroplanes are long.

Alexander Longshaw (6)

Perry Wood Primary & Nursery School, Worcester

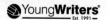

Olivia

O ranges are juicy
L ove unicorns
I love my mum and dad
V acuum is loud
I ce is cold
A pples are tasty.

Olivia Ann Davis (6)
Perry Wood Primary & Nursery School, Worcester

Rabbit

R abbit runs

A ll fluffy and cute

B ounces all around

B oing, boing

I love rabbits

T witchy, twitchy.

Lacie Broughton (6)

Perry Wood Primary & Nursery School, Worcester

Horses

H ay
O range horses
R oll in the mud
S urviving the cold
E ats all day
S leeps all day.

Maddison Grant (6)

Perry Wood Primary & Nursery School, Worcester

Cars

C ows are my favourite
A pples are healthy
R eindeer are sweet
S nakes are scary.

Kasey Jay Morris (6)

Perry Wood Primary & Nursery School, Worcester

Just

J ust help them
U mbrella for the rain
S nakes are long
T ake cover.

Joshua Mason (6)

Perry Wood Primary & Nursery School, Worcester

Ivy

I love my mummy
V iolet is my favourite colour
Y o-yo tricks I like to do.

Ivy Smith (6)
Perry Wood Primary & Nursery School, Worcester

Dodgeball

D odging yellow fat balls

O ld balls running wild in the park

D odging balls that someone threw

G eorgia has jumping balls

E veryone loves dodgeball

B ouncing balls everywhere in my house

A larming balls that hit you in the face

L earning balls that are intelligent

L onely balls that have been thrown out of sight.

Max Maclean (7)

Ramsgate Holy Trinity CE (A) Primary School, Broadstairs

Dinosaur

D inosaurs like to eat plants and meat

I n the olden days, dinosaurs roamed for 200 million years

N o dinosaurs now exist in the world

O n their back, they have dried blood

S ome dinosaurs eat fish

A ll of the dinos fight

U tahraptor is the biggest raptor dinosaur

R oarosaurus is the loudest!

George William Cox (6)

Ramsgate Holy Trinity CE (A) Primary School, Broadstairs

Teaching

T eddy loves to teach
E veryone thinks Teddy is a genius
A pples are nice, so Teddy eats them
C lever people like maths
H angry teachers are not clever
I like writing
N ever guess in maths
G reat work.

Olivia Grace Garratt (7)

Ramsgate Holy Trinity CE (A) Primary School, Broadstairs

Unicorn

U nicorns are pretty

N aughty people are mean to unicorns

I n the country, unicorns like the sun

C an you catch a unicorn?

O h, I love unicorns

R ainbow the unicorn

N o one can be mean to unicorns.

Poppy Maclean (7)
Ramsgate Holy Trinity CE (A) Primary School, Broadstairs

Unicorn

U nicorns are my favourite
N o, I like unicorns, not tigers
I don't like corn
C an you catch a unicorn?
O h, I love that unicorn
"R idiculous unicorn," said mum
N ot a horse again.

Alice Guan (6)

Ramsgate Holy Trinity CE (A) Primary School,
Broadstairs

Mermaid

M ermaids are pretty

E very girl likes mermaids

R emember lots of girls like mermaids

M ermaids are shiny

A nd a boy likes mermaids

I like lots of mermaids

D anger is a shark to a mermaid.

Lola Mathews (6)

Ramsgate Holy Trinity CE (A) Primary School, Broadstairs

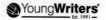

Georgia

G eorgia is lovely
E veryone is her friend
O ranges are my favourite
R unning is my favourite sport
G eorgia is amazing
I love unicorns
A lice is my favourite friend.

Georgia Louise Youngs (7)

Ramsgate Holy Trinity CE (A) Primary School,
Broadstairs

Puffins

P uffins are pretty

U nderwater, puffins swim with fins

F ine and pretty puffins

F it puffins

I n the water, puffins swim

N ice and kind puffins

S ensitive puffins.

Esmée Rose Denton (6)

Ramsgate Holy Trinity CE (A) Primary School, Broadstairs

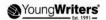
Writing

W riting is my favourite
R hubarb is my favourite
I like hard work
T rying is good for writing
I don't like pencil crayon
N eed neat work
G et a pencil.

Amber Thompson (6)

Ramsgate Holy Trinity CE (A) Primary School,
Broadstairs

Reading

R ed books I love

E verybody loves books

A person like me will love books

D elightful books

I love lots of books

N ew books are good

G reat books.

Emily Batcheler (6)

Ramsgate Holy Trinity CE (A) Primary School, Broadstairs

Tennis

T ennis is my favourite sport
E verybody likes tennis
N obody has a racket
N othing happened at tennis
I t looks like the match is on
S omeone has a ball.

Zach Ryan Evans-Hunt (6)

Ramsgate Holy Trinity CE (A) Primary School,
Broadstairs

Gaming

G ames are playful

A iming at people

M ario Kart 2 has lots of characters

I come second every time

N ames like Yoshi are on Mario Kart

G ames are fun.

Finlay Collins (6)

Ramsgate Holy Trinity CE (A) Primary School, Broadstairs

Aliens

A rainbow-coloured scary alien
L ives in space
I t is magic
E arth is his favourite place
N oisy screaming alien
S itting in his spaceship.

Peter Tovell (6)

Ramsgate Holy Trinity CE (A) Primary School,
Broadstairs

Unicorn

U nicorns are beautiful

N ice unicorns

I love unicorns

C olourful unicorns

O range unicorns

R acing unicorns

N ight, unicorns.

Freya June Maxted (6)

Ramsgate Holy Trinity CE (A) Primary School, Broadstairs

Rafting

R acing fast

A cting speedy

F ast and speedy

T rying to slow down

I nteresting facts

N ice doing sport

G oing to do sport.

Samuel Kane (6)

Ramsgate Holy Trinity CE (A) Primary School, Broadstairs

Nature

N ature is fantastic

A nts

T ry to climb a tree

U gly bugs

R ed bugs, green bugs, lots of bugs

E very day you see an insect.

Evelyn Michael (7)

Ramsgate Holy Trinity CE (A) Primary School, Broadstairs

Beach

B ig bones are everywhere
E verybody is friends
A friend played with me
C rabs pinch me a lot
H ardly made a sandcastle.

Liam Cannon (6)

Ramsgate Holy Trinity CE (A) Primary School,
Broadstairs

Trying

T rying, learning

R acing car

Y aks

I like marshmallows

N an loves me

G anoc, my stuffed animal, likes me.

Dolcie Thorn (6)

Ramsgate Holy Trinity CE (A) Primary School, Broadstairs

Movies

M y family loves me
O h, that looks yucky
V ery quiet in the cinema
I loved the cinema
E very film I watch.

Finlay McAlister (6)

Ramsgate Holy Trinity CE (A) Primary School,
Broadstairs

James

J ames loves jogging

A nimals love James

M um loves me

E lephants hate me

S am is my best friend.

James Bryan Greensted (6)

Ramsgate Holy Trinity CE (A) Primary School,
Broadstairs

Teddy

T he best kicker
E verybody cheers
D ogs are savage
D ragons are cool
Y elling lion.

Teddy Meise (7)

Ramsgate Holy Trinity CE (A) Primary School, Broadstairs

Ayomide

A good line leader
Y elling at my brother
O ranges are juicy
M oon at night
I am chatty
D on't like dogs
E xcellent boy.

Ayomide Roland (6)
St James' Primary School, Paisley

Aaron

A mazing at ABCs
A lso at maths
R ight all the time
O ranges are nice
N inety-nine is a good number.

Aaron McEwan (6)
St James' Primary School, Paisley

Cameron

C andy

A nimals

M aths

E lephants

R hino

O ranges

N ever cheeky.

Cameron Thomson (6)
St James' Primary School, Paisley

Robyn

R oly-poly
O ver the rainbow
B uying a dress
Y ellow lemons
N ice girl.

Robyn Borris (5)
St James' Primary School, Paisley

Zack

Z ebras are crazy
A pples are tasty
C ats are cute
K icking footballs is fun.

Zack Nugent (6)

St James' Primary School, Paisley

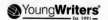

Liam

L ucky is my bird
I ce cream and Flake
A mazing at maths
M y mum is great.

Liam Sweeney (6)
St James' Primary School, Paisley

Ross

R ed is a good colour

O ctober is Halloween

S haring my Lego

S uper boy.

Ross McFadyen (5)

St James' Primary School, Paisley

Keira

K angaroo
E lephant
I ce cream
R abbit
A nt.

Keira Reader (6)

St James' Primary School, Paisley

David

D ogs
A wesome
V ans
 I ce cream
D inosaurs.

David Adetoyosi Adekanmbi (6)

St James' Primary School, Paisley

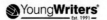

Logan

L og
O ranges
G iggle
A mazing
N aughty.

Logan Flanagan (6)
St James' Primary School, Paisley

Lara

L ove
A dorable
R eally like Minecraft
A mazing.

Lara Reis (6)

St James' Primary School, Paisley

Tye

T errific
Y oung
E nergetic.

Tye David McLeod (6)

St James' Primary School, Paisley

Ben

B asketball

E nergy

N ice.

Ben Deatcher (6)

St James' Primary School, Paisley

Millie Jones

M y favourite toy is my squishy
I love my brother
L ollies are my favourite
L ove seeing my baby cousin
I love reading my books
E njoy riding my bike

J umping around too much makes me dizzy
O ften excited
N ever be nasty to other people
E njoy playing with my friends
S chool is amazing.

Millie Jones (6)

Yealmpstone Farm Primary School, Plympton

My Brother

H e is part of my family

A fter school, he will go to diving

R unning around and playing football

R eally good at sports

Y ou are cheeky but really deep down, you are nice

J oking around with me (Oliver)

A t home, he helps me to learn

C ounting my times tables together

K ind, my brother, Harry!

Oliver Sluman (6)
Yealmpstone Farm Primary School, Plympton

Love My Mummy

L ove my mummy lots
O n Saturdays I have a film night
V ans are red
E very day is cool

M ummies are the best
Y ellow boats are good

M ark is my daddy's name
U nicorns are the best
M y brother is Nathan
M y mummy is called Sue
Y ou are the best.

Leighton Sindall (7)
Yealmpstone Farm Primary School, Plympton

Lilah-Rose

L ollipops are my favourite
I love my pets
L .O.L. dolls rock
A melia is my big sister
H olidays to Greece are the best

R oses are my favourite flowers
O ne day I want to be a vet
S eth is my boyfriend
E verybody likes music in my house.

Lilah-Rose Hobbs (6)

Yealmpstone Farm Primary School, Plympton

Football

F ootball is my favourite sport
O n the pitch, I score a goal
O n the bench, I cheer my team
T he other team may score a goal
B ut then I score again
A t half-time, the coach says well done
L ots of cheers from everyone
L ove the game of football.

Harrison Smith (6)

Yealmpstone Farm Primary School, Plympton

Seth And Lilah Rose

L ilah Rose makes me smile

I love Lilah Rose

L ilah Rose loves me all the time

A nice girl

H ugs and kisses all the time

R ed hair and rosy cheeks

O ne in a million

S eth loves Lilah Rose

E very day she loves me more.

Seth Jonathan Williams (6)

Yealmpstone Farm Primary School, Plympton

Jackson

J ackson is the best little brother

A ll the things we do together make me happy

C uddles with him are my favourite

K icking a football makes him laugh

S ometimes I read to him

O n the slide, we go down

N obody could be better.

Olivia Gibson (6)

Yealmpstone Farm Primary School, Plympton

Hungry

H arvey eats too much

U mbrellas are used for keeping my food dry

N ovember is a good time to eat warm food

G ranny and Grandad let us have lots of pudding

R uby, my cuddly toy, is my best toy ever

Y ummy tea and pudding.

Evie Stemp (7)

Yealmpstone Farm Primary School, Plympton

Matthew

M akes people smile around him
A ctive, loves playing sports
T houghtful and caring
T rusting and loving
H ardworking, always tries his best
E nergetic
W onderful and warm-hearted.

Matthew Jones (7)

Yealmpstone Farm Primary School, Plympton

Eve

F orever together
R eading exciting books together
I love playing with toys with my friends
E xcitement when I am playing games
N ever alone
D iving in the sea
S ecret messages.

Eve Leia Hanrahan (6)

Yealmpstone Farm Primary School, Plympton

Sophie

S ophie is my name

O dd Squad is my favourite TV show

P eter Rabbit is my brother's favourite show

H arlyn Sands is my favourite place

I love my mummy

E ggs, I like them scrambled.

Sophie Nightingale (6)

Yealmpstone Farm Primary School, Plympton

Mummy

M y favourite colour is purple
U nder my bed I have lots of toys
M y favourite food is a roast dinner
M y favourite toy is slime
Y ellow is the colour of my hair.

Scarlett Evans (7)
Yealmpstone Farm Primary School, Plympton

Sister

S weet baby sister
I can't wait to meet you
S o we can play
T ogether every day
E ven when you are crying
R emember I love you.

Taylor Holmes (6)

Yealmpstone Farm Primary School, Plympton

Evie

E very night, before I go to bed, I have a story

V ery excited to go away this weekend

I want to be a vet when I grow up

E ach weekend I go on my bike.

Evie Lilgan (6)

Yealmpstone Farm Primary School, Plympton

My Dog, Lenny

L abradoodles are nice and friendly
E verybody loves Lenny
N ibbles our slippers
N eeds a brush
Y ummy treats, he is good.

Emilia Mills (6)

Yealmpstone Farm Primary School, Plympton

Daddy

D addy goes to work a lot

A nd he fixes helicopters

D addy has funny jokes

D addy is fun

Y ou are the best.

Freya Deady (6)

Yealmpstone Farm Primary School, Plympton

Faith

F riendship is about love
A nd respect
I love my family
T o the moon and back
H appily ever after.

Faith Ella English (7)

Yealmpstone Farm Primary School, Plympton

Drama

D is for dancing

R is rhythm

A cting fun

M y favourite thing

A laddin is the best.

Eloise Walker (6)

Yealmpstone Farm Primary School, Plympton

Lego

L ove my mummy

E ve loves me

G ames are good fun

O liver is my friend.

Ben Robinson (7)

Yealmpstone Farm Primary School, Plympton

Cat

C ats are cute

A lways meowing

T hey have sharp teeth.

Finley Mark Whiting (7)

Yealmpstone Farm Primary School, Plympton

young Writers
information

We hope you have enjoyed reading this book – and that you will continue to in the coming years.

If you're a young writer who enjoys reading and creative writing, or the parent of an enthusiastic poet or story writer, do visit our website **www.youngwriters.co.uk**. Here you will find free competitions, workshops and games, as well as recommended reads, a poetry glossary and our blog. There's lots to keep budding writers motivated to write!

If you would like to order further copies of this book, or any of our other titles, then please give us a call or order via your online account.

Young Writers
Remus House
Coltsfoot Drive
Peterborough
PE2 9BF
(01733) 890066
info@youngwriters.co.uk

Join in the conversation!
Tips, news, giveaways and much more!

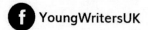 **YoungWritersUK**    **@YoungWritersCW**